Calico Pie
and other poems

Compiled by Tig Thomas

Miles Kelly

First published in 2010 by Miles Kelly Publishing Ltd
Harding's Barn, Bardfield End Green, Thaxted, Essex, CM6 3PX, UK

2 4 6 8 10 9 7 5 3 1

Editorial Director Belinda Gallagher

Art Director Jo Cowan

Assistant Editor Claire Philip

Designer Joe Jones

Junior Designer Kayleigh Allen

Production Manager Elizabeth Collins

Reprographics Stephan Davis, Ian Paulyn

ISBN 978-1-84810-372-6

Printed in China

British Library Cataloguing-in-Publication Data
A catalogue record for this book is available from the British Library

ACKNOWLEDGEMENTS

The publishers would like to thank Kirsten Wilson for
the illustrations she contributed to this book.

All other artwork from the Miles Kelly Artwork Bank

The publishers would like to thank bluesky/Fotolia.com
for the use of their photograph on page 6

Made with paper from a sustainable forest

www.mileskelly.net
info@mileskelly.net

www.factsforprojects.com

Self-publish your
children's book

buddingpress.co.uk

Contents

The Moon's the North Wind's Cookie

The Moon's the North Wind's cookie
He bites it, day by day,
Until there's but a rim of scraps
That crumble all away.

The South Wind is a baker.
He kneads clouds in his den,
And bakes a crisp new moon that greedy

North . . . Wind . . . eats . . . again!

Vachel Lindsay

From *Karamos*

The Wind blows east,
The Wind blows west,
The blue eggs in the robin's nest
Will soon have wings and beak and breast
And flutter and fly away.

Henry Wadsworth Longfellow

Wind

Little wind, blow on the hill top,
Little wind, blow down the plain;
Little wind, blow up the sunshine,
Little wind, blow off the rain.

Kate Greenaway

Summer is Coming

"Summer is coming, summer is coming,
I know it, I know it, I know it.
Light again, leaf again, life again, love again,"
Yes, my wild little poet.

Sing the new year in under the blue.
Last year you sang it as gladly.
"New, new, new, new!" Is it then so new
That you should carol so madly?

"Love again, song again, nest again, young again,"
Never a prophet so crazy!
And hardly a daisy as yet, little friend,
See, there is hardly a daisy.

"Here again, here, here, here, happy year!"
O warble unchidden, unbidden!
Summer is coming, is coming, my dear,
And all the winters are hidden.

Alfred, Lord Tennyson

From *Summer Days*

Winter is cold-hearted;
Spring is yea and nay;
Autumn is a weathercock,
Blown every way:
Summer days for me,
When every leaf is on its tree.

Christina Rossetti

Seal Lullaby

Oh! Hush thee, my baby, the night is behind us,
And black are the waters that sparkled so green.
The moon, o'er the combers, looks downward to find us
At rest in the hollows that rustle between.
Where billow meets billow, there soft be thy pillow;
Ah, weary wee flipperling, curl at thy ease!
The storm shall not wake thee, nor shark overtake thee,
Asleep in the arms of the slow-swinging seas.

Rudyard Kipling

Combers big waves

Seals sleep floating just under the water and can come up to breathe without waking up.

The Ant

My child, observe the useful Ant,
How hard she works each day.
She works as hard as adamant
(That's very hard, they say).
She has no time to gallivant;
She has no time to play.
Let Fido chase his tail all day;
Let Kitty play at tag:
She has no time to throw away,
She has no tail to wag.
She scurries round from morn till night;
She never, never sleeps;
She seizes everything in sight,
And drags it home with all her might,
And all she takes she keeps.

Oliver Herford

My Heart's in the Highlands

My heart's in the Highlands, my heart is not here;

My heart's in the Highlands a-chasing the deer;

Chasing the wild deer, and following the roe,

My heart's in the Highlands wherever I go.

Farewell to the Highlands, farewell to the North,

The birthplace of valour, the country of worth;

Wherever I wander, wherever I rove,

The hills of the Highlands for ever I love.

The Highlands are a beautiful, mountainous region in the far north of Scotland. In this poem, the speaker is remembering the place he loves but has had to leave.

Farewell to the mountains high covered with snow;
Farewell to the straths and green valleys below;
Farewell to the forests and wild hanging woods;
Farewell to the torrents and loud-pouring floods.
My heart's in the Highlands, my heart is not here,
My heart's in the Highlands a-chasing the deer;
Chasing the wild deer, and following the roe,
My heart's in the Highlands wherever I go.

Robert Burns

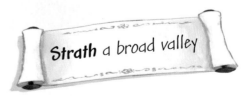

Strath a broad valley

A Flower Alphabet

A for the Aconite, first of the year,
    With its pretty green ruff and its message of cheer.

B for the Buttercup, able to hold
    Dewdrop and rain in its chalice of gold.

C for the Cowslip, sweet joy of the spring;
    When cowslips are blooming the nightingales sing.

D for the Daisy, white star of the grass,
    Lifting its bright eye to us as we pass.

E for the Eglantine, lovely wild rose,
    Sheds fragrance of sweetbriar wherever it grows.

F for the Foxglove, the sentinel tall,
    Guarding the forest from summer to fall.

G for the Gorse of rich golden delight;
    Linnaeus went down on his knees at the sight.

Buttercup

Eglantine

Linnaeus was an 18th century scientist who worked out the system for naming plants and animals that is still used today.

Iris

H for the Harebell, so fragile, yet strong
  The dear little Bluebells of Scotland in song.

I for the Iris which grows by the stream,
  The flower of the Rainbow, how golden its gleam!

J for St John's Wort, of medical fame,
  Balm of the Warrior's Wound was its name.

K for the Kingcup that loves marshy fields,
  And glorious the harvest of gold that it yields!

L for the Ling, the dear flower of the heath,
  How tender its colour, how fragrant its breath!

M for the Meadowsweet, pleasant and rare
  Is the perfume with which it enchanteth the air!

Ling another name for heather

Nightshade

N for the Nightshade, or Bittersweet, flower,
   With its berries and blossoms of
   poisonous power.

O for the Oxlip, a flower that you'll find
   When cowslips and orchids in posies you bind.

P for the Primrose, recalling to sight
   Paths in the woodlands a-shimmer with light.

Q for the Quaking grass, name that it takes
   From the way it unceasingly shivers and shakes.

R for the Rest-harrow, staying the plough,
   Food for the gentle-eyed, ruminant cow.

S for the Speedwell, of tenderest blue;
   From the skies it has taken its exquisite hue.

Speedwell

T for the Traveller's Joy that you'll find
   Where sweet, sheltering hedgerows wander and wind.

Windflower

U for the Upright Sea-lavender flower;
The sand-swallows claim it for
sheltering bower.

V for the Violet, flower of the soul,
Heart's-ease of Paradise, making us whole.

W for Windflower, so fair to the sight,
That throws o'er the woodlands her mantle
of light.

X forms a cross in the Passion-flower wild
In Southern America, balmy and mild.

Y for the Yarrow, all wayfarers know,
As it grows by the wayside wherever you go.

Z is the ribbon this posy to bind,
With the thoughts and the fragrance it brings
to your mind.

Anonymous

Ducks' Ditty

All along the backwater,
Through the rushes tall,
Ducks are a-dabbling,
Up tails all.

Ducks' tails, drake's tails,
Yellow feet a-quiver,
Yellow bills all out of sight,
Busy in the river!

16

Slushy green undergrowth
Where the roach swim –
Here we keep our larder,
Cool and full and dim.

Everyone for what he likes!
We like to be
Heads down, tails up,
Dabbling free!

High in the blue above
Swifts whirl and call –
We are down a-dabbling,
Up tails all.

Kenneth Grahame

A Lark

Lark-bird, lark-bird, soaring high,
Are you never weary?
When you reach the empty sky
Are the clouds not dreary?
Don't you sometimes long to be
A silent goldfish in the sea?

Goldfish, goldfish, diving deep,
Are you never sad, say?
When you feel the cold waves creep
Are you really glad, say?
Don't you sometimes long to sing
And be a lark-bird on the wing?

Lawrence Alma-Tadema

The Cat of Cats

I am the cat of cats. I am
The everlasting cat!
Cunning, and old, and sleek as jam,
The everlasting cat!
I hunt vermin in the night –
The everlasting cat!
For I see best without the light –
The everlasting cat!

William Brighty Rands

Robin the Bobbin

Robin the Bobbin, the big-bellied Ben,
He ate more meat than fourscore men;
He ate a cow, he ate a calf,
He ate a butcher and a half;
He ate a church, he ate a steeple,
He ate the priest and all
   the people!
A cow and a calf,
An ox and a half,
A church and a steeple,
And all the good people,
And yet he complained that his
   stomach wasn't full.

Anonymous

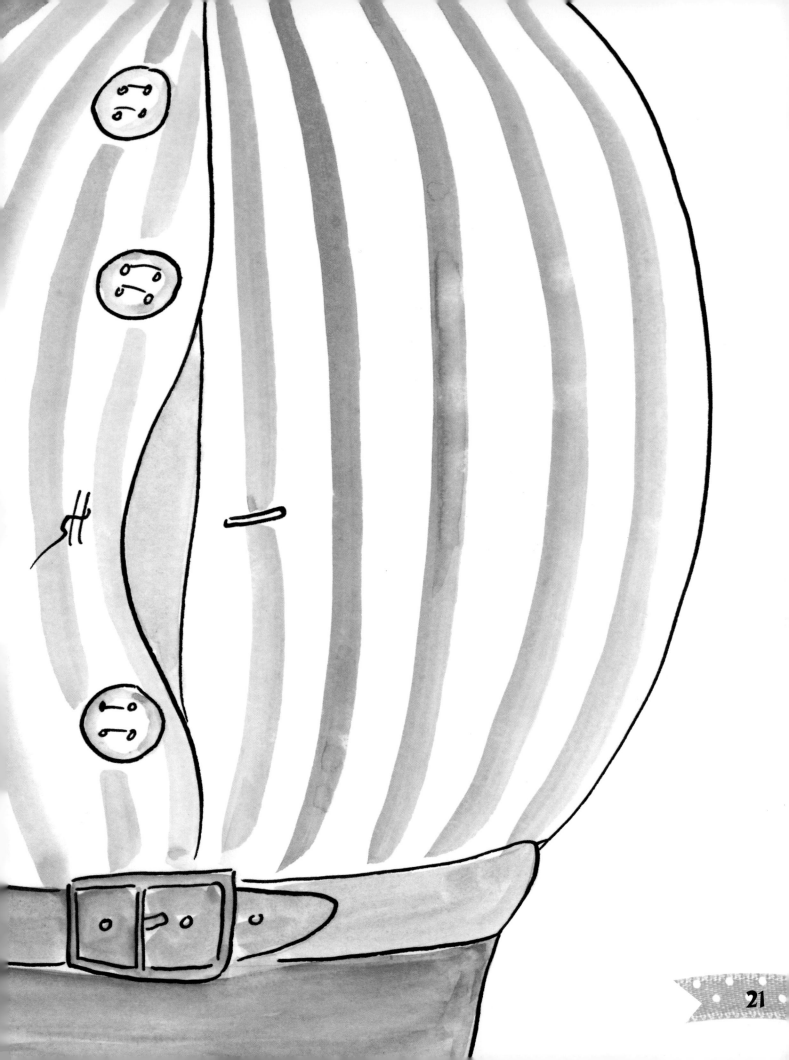

Over in the Meadow

Over in the meadow,
In the sand in the sun,
Lived an old mother toadie,
And her little toadie one,
"Wink!" said the mother;
"I wink!" said the one,
So they winked and they blinked,
In the sand in the sun.

Over in the meadow,
Where the stream runs blue,
Lived an old mother fish,
And her little fishes two,
"Swim!" said the mother;
"We swim!" said the two,
So they swam and they leaped,
Where the stream runs blue.

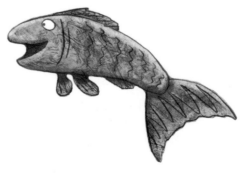

Over in the meadow,
In a hole in a tree,
Lived an old mother bluebird,
And her little birdies three,
"**Sing!**" said the mother;
"We sing!" said the three,
So they sang and were glad,
In a hole in the tree.

Over in the meadow,
In the reeds on the shore,
Lived an old mother muskrat,
And her little ratties four,
"**Dive!**" said the mother;
"We dive!" said the four,
So they dived and they burrowed,
In the reeds on the shore.

Over in the meadow,
In a snug beehive,
Lived a mother honey bee,
And her little bees five,
"Buzz!" said the mother;
"We buzz!" said the five,
So they buzzed and they hummed,
In the snug beehive.

Over in the meadow,
In a nest built of sticks,
Lived a black mother crow,
And her little crows six,
"Caw!" said the mother;
"We caw!" said the six,
So they cawed and they called,
In their nest built of sticks.

24

Over in the meadow,
Where the grass is so even,
Lived a gay mother cricket,
And her little crickets seven,
"Chirp!" said the mother;
"We chirp!" said the seven,
So they chirped cheery notes,
In the grass soft and even.

Over in the meadow,
By the old mossy gate,
Lived a brown mother lizard,
And her little lizards eight,
"Bask!" said the mother;
"We bask!" said the eight,
So they basked in the sun,
On the old mossy gate.

Over in the meadow,
Where the quiet pools shine,
Lived a green mother frog,
And her little froggies nine,
"**Croak!**" said the mother;
"We croak!" said the nine,
So they croaked and they splashed,
Where the quiet pools shine.

Over in the meadow,
In a sly little den,
Lived a grey mother spider,
And her little spiders ten,
"**Spin!**" said the mother;
"We spin!" said the ten,
So they spun lacy webs,
In their sly little den.

Olive A Wadsworth

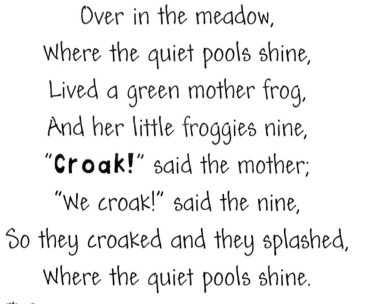
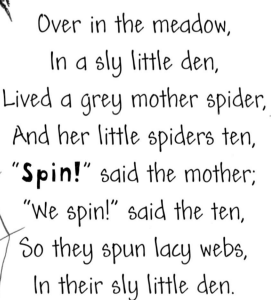

26

From *Rain in Summer*

How beautiful is the rain!
After the dust and heat,
In the broad and fiery street,
In the narrow lane,
How beautiful is the rain!

How it clatters along the roofs,
Like the tramp of hoofs
How it gushes and struggles out
From the throat of the overflowing spout!

Across the window-pane
It pours and pours;
And swift and wide,
With a muddy tide,
Like a river down the gutter roars
The rain, the welcome rain!

Henry Wadsworth Longfellow

27

Hospitality

Said a Snake to a Frog with a wrinkled skin,
"As I notice, dear, that your dress is thin,
And a rain is coming, I'll take you in."

John Bannister Tabb

The Dog

Here is the Dog. Since time began,
The Dog has been the friend of man,
The Dog loves man because he shears
His coat and clips his tail and ears.
Man loves the Dog because he'll stay
And listen to his talk all day,
And wag his tail and show delight
At all his jokes, however trite.
His bark is far worse than his bite,
So people say. They may be right;
Yet if to make a choice I had,
I'd choose his bark, however bad.

Oliver Herford

From A Make Believe

I will think as thinks the rabbit:
Let the wind chafe
In the trees overhead,
We are quite safe
In our dark, yellow bed!
Let the rain pour!
It never can bore
A hole in our roof —
It is waterproof!
So is the cloak
We always carry,
We furry folk,
In sandhole or
        quarry!

It is perfect bliss
To lie in a nest
So soft as this,
All so warmly drest!
No one to flurry you!
No one to hurry you!
No one to scurry you!
Holes plenty to creep in!
All day to sleep in!
All night to roam in!
Grey dawn to run home in!
And all the days and nights to
come after —
All the tomorrows for hind-legs
and laughter!

George Macdonald

Bird Songs

I will sing a song,
Said the owl.
You sing a song, sing-song
Ugly fowl!
What will you sing about,
Night in and day out?

All about the night,
When the grey
With her cloak smothers bright,
Hard, sharp day.
Oh, the moon! The cool dew!
And the shadows! – **tu-whoo!**

I will sing a song,
Said the nightingale.
Sing a song, long, long,
Little Neverfail!
What will you sing about,
Day in or day out?

All about the light
Gone away,
Down, away, and out of sight:
Wake up, day!
For the master is not dead,
Only gone to bed.

I will sing a song,
Said the lark.
Sing, sing, Throat-strong,
Little Kill-the-dark!
What will you sing about,
Day in and night out?

I can only call!
I can't think!
Let me up, that's all!
I see a chink!
I've been thirsting all night
For the glorious light!

George Macdonald

Calico Pie

Calico Pie,
The little Birds fly
Down to the calico tree,
Their wings were blue,
And they sang "Tilly-loo!"
Till away they flew, —
And they never came back to me!

They never came back!
They never came back!
They never came back to me!

Calico Jam,
The little Fish swam,
Over the syllabub sea,
He took off his hat,
To the Sole and the Sprat,
And the Willeby-Wat, —
But he never came back to me!

He never came back!
He never came back!
He never came back to me!

Calico Ban,
The little Mice ran,
To be ready in time for tea,
Flippity flup,
They drank it all up,
And danced in the cup, –
But they never came back to me!

They never came back!
They never came back!
They never came back to me!

Calico Drum,
The Grasshoppers come,
The Butterfly, Beetle, and Bee,
Over the ground,
Around and around,
With a hop and a bound, –
But they never came back to me!

They never came back!
They never came back!
They never came back to me!

Edward Lear

A Friend in the Garden

He is not John the gardener,
And yet the whole day long
Employs himself most usefully,
The flowerbeds among.

He is not Tom the pussy-cat,
And yet the other day,
With stealthy stride and glistening eye,
He crept upon his prey.

He is not Dash the dear old dog,
And yet, perhaps, if you
Took pains with him and petted him,
You'd come to love him too.

He's not a Blackbird, though he chirps,
And though he once was black;
And now he wears a loose grey coat,
All wrinkled on the back.

He's got a very dirty face,
And very shining eyes!
He sometimes comes and sits indoors;
He looks – and p'r'aps is – wise.

But in a sunny flowerbed
He has his fixed abode;
He eats the things that eat my plants –
He is a friendly **TOAD**.

Juliana Horatia Ewing

Toads are very popular with gardeners because they eat slugs and beetles, which would otherwise eat the plants.

Sleep, Baby

Sleep, baby, sleep!
The large stars are the sheep;
The little stars are the lambs, I guess,
The bright moon is the shepherdess.
Sleep, baby, sleep.

Elizabeth Prentiss

My Bed is a Boat

My bed is like a little boat;
Nurse helps me in when I embark;
She girds me in my sailor's coat
And starts me in the dark.
At night I go on board and say
Goodnight to all my friends on shore;
I shut my eyes and sail away
And see and hear no more.
And sometimes things to bed I take,
As prudent sailors have to do;
Perhaps a slice of wedding-cake,
Perhaps a toy or two.
All night across the dark we steer;
But when the day returns at last,
Safe in my room beside the pier,
I find my vessel fast.

Robert Louis Stevenson

Gird to wrap up

Index of First Lines